CULTURE IN ACTION

Movie Special Effects

Liz Miles

www.raintreepublishers.co.uk
Visit our website to find out more information about Raintree books.

To order:
☎ Phone +44 (0) 1865 888066
Fax +44 (0) 1865 314091
Visit www.raintreepublishers.co.uk

Raintree is an imprint of Capstone Global Library Limited, a company incorporated in England and Wales having its registered office at 7 Pilgrim Street, London, EC4V 6LB – Registered company number: 6695582

First published in hardback in 2010

Edited by Louise Galpine, Rachel Howells, and Helen Cox
Designed by Kimberly Miracle and Betsy Wernert
Original illustrations © Capstone Global Library Ltd.
Illustrated by kja-artists.com
Picture research by Hannah Taylor
Production by Alison Parsons
Originated by Dot Gradations Ltd.
Printed in China by CTPS.

ISBN 978 1 406212 04 4
14 13 12 11 10
10 9 8 7 6 5 4 3 2 1

British Library Cataloguing in Publication Data
Miles, Elizabeth
Movie Special Effects. – (Culture in action)
778.5'345
A full catalogue record for this book is available from the British Library.

Acknowledgements

We would like to thank the following for permission to reproduce photographs: akg-images pp. **5** (Walt Disney Pictures), **25 left** (New Line Productions); Corbis pp. **16** (Louie Psihoyos), **17** (Louis Quail); Getty Images pp. **7** (Mark Mainz), **18** (Hulton Archive/ John Kobal Foundation); Rex Features pp. **4** (Everett Collection), **6** (On Location News), **10** (Charles Sykes), **11** (Action Press), **12** (ITV), **20** and **26** (Everett/ © Universal); The Kobal Collection pp. **8** (Danjaq/ Eon/ UA), **14**, **25 right**, and **29** (New Line Cinema), **15** (20th century Fox/ Paramount/ Digital Domain), **22** (Cinema Center), **24** (New Line/ Saul Zaentz/ Wing Nut Films), **28** (Dreamworks/ Universal); The Ronald Grant Archive pp. **9** (Impact Pictures), **19** (© Courtesy of Warner Bros. Ent/ DC Comics), **23** (Canal+/ Carolco Pictures/ Lightstorm Entertainment/ Pacific Western).

Icon and banner images supplied by Shutterstock: © Alexander Lukin, © ornitopter, © Colorlife, and © David S. Rose.

Cover photograph of stuntman jumping through wall of fire, reproduced with permission of Corbis (Jamie Budge).

We would like to thank George Zwierzynski Jr., Jackie Murphy, and Nancy Harris for their invaluable help in the preparation of this book.

Contents

Introduction	4
Stunts	6
Fires and storms	10
Sets and models	14
Sequencing and mixing	18
Amazing make-up	22
CGI	24
Award winners	28
Glossary	30
Find out more	31
Index	32

Some words are printed in bold, **like this**. You can find out what they mean by looking in the glossary on page 30.

Introduction

In a way, every movie is one big "special effect". When we watch a movie, our brains tell us we are watching a moving world. In fact, we are watching a series of still pictures.

The "movie effect"

At most cinemas, in just one second, 24 still pictures are projected onto the screen. Our brains turn all the pictures into one continuous moving image. The brain can do this because our eye remembers each picture for a short time after it has passed, so we still remember one picture when the next is shown. The brain can join the pictures together, without any gaps between.

Few special effects were available in the 1930s. In *The Wizard of Oz* (1939), the lion was an actor in a costume.

Today, special effects include computer-generated, talking animals, like Aslan in *The Chronicles of Narnia: The Lion, The Witch, and The Wardrobe* (2005).

Mechanical and digital effects

Complicated special effects make today's movies exciting and realistic. Effects filmed on the **set** (scenery used for films) are called **mechanical effects**. They involve trained **stunt performers**, who film the dangerous parts of the film, and expensive equipment. **Digital effects** are special effects made with computers. For example, **CGI** (computer-generated imagery) can make realistic, moving monsters.

The "stop" trick

The first ever special effect was in *The Execution of Mary, Queen of Scots*. The film was made in 1895 by Alfred Clark. The actress playing Mary knelt to be beheaded. The executioner brought down an axe to just above her neck. The actors then froze and the camera stopped filming. The actress was replaced with a dummy. Filming restarted and the executioner finished the "beheading". He then picked up the dummy's gruesome head for all to see.

Stunts

A stunt is any dangerous act in a movie, ranging from a fall to a car chase. Rich and famous actors and actresses are irreplaceable. If they break a leg or twist an ankle while filming a blockbuster movie, millions of dollars could be lost – the movie might never be finished. So **stunt performers** usually do the dangerous bits.

Hidden talent

The stunt performers are not even noticed. During a stunt, they are filmed from behind, or from far enough away that their faces cannot be seen clearly. They may wear a mask to make them look like the star whose part they are playing. **Close-ups** of the star are added later, so that viewers think it is the star who did the stunts.

Safety

When a stunt is being prepared, the **stunt co-ordinator** checks to make sure the equipment is safe. Stunt performers are specially trained. They have to be athletic, strong, and able to use complicated equipment safely.

Stunt performers learn how to land safely. An awkward fall can strain a muscle or break a bone.

Stunt tricks

Stunts involve specific equipment:

Ejection – A kicker ramp throws a person upwards (such as after an explosion). Compressed (squashed) air makes the ramp shoot upwards at the press of a button.

Fall – A carefully planned fall is made safe by tying ropes to the person. Ropes are removed digitally from the film later. Hidden cardboard boxes, airbags, and padded clothing lessen the impact of the landing.

Flight – To make a person appear to fly, a strong harness and ropes lift and move the person through the air.

A stunt performer took over from Tobey Maguire during the filming of this scene in *Spider Man 2*. Safety wires support both actors, but were digitally removed from the film later.

Warning:

Never try any stunt yourself. You must have specialist training and advice from a qualified adult.

Car-chase stunts

Most action movies involve a chase – often in cars. Stunt car drivers are carefully trained and one car chase can take weeks to film. Parts of a car chase are usually practised first, at very low speeds.

Safety is a major concern, so the driver wears protective clothing and the cars are specially built. A metal frame inside the car protects the driver from getting injured if the car rolls. Planned rolls are common in car chases. For example, in the Bond movie, *Casino Royale*, Bond's car rolled seven times in one scene. To make cars roll, a ramp shoots up from the ground when the driver presses a button. The ramp pushes the car over. Ramps are also used to make cars leap.

A trained stunt driver took the wheel for this car roll on ice in the James Bond movie, *Die Another Day*.

Props

Props keep stunt performers safe. Special safety glass shatters into tiny cubes, so that it does not cause injury to a stunt performer who has to be thrown through a window. A pile of foam bricks can fall on anyone without leaving a mark.

A motorcyclist stunt driver smashes through a window. Safety glass for stunts is often made from sugar.

Do you want to be a stunt performer?

After leaving school or college you must go on a course that trains stunt performers. While you are at school, it is useful to learn skills such as martial arts, rock-climbing, or other action sports.

Dedication is essential. It's a tough job with long hours. Conditions are often uncomfortable. Imagine, for example, having to walk through fire . . .

Fires and storms

Action and adventure movies need lots of drama, such as explosions, fireballs, floods, and landslides. They also need **atmosphere** – violent storms or mysterious mists are perfect for building suspense. Many of these effects can be created and filmed on **set**, using some amazing machines and materials.

Fire

Real fires get out of control easily. The damage is instant and the risk of injury or death is very high. On-set movie fires must be under the complete control of a **pyrotechnician**.

To film a burning house, fuel tanks are hidden inside the building. These burn to give the flames, but they can be turned on and off from a safe distance.

A carefully controlled fire in a New York apartment – used for the filming of *Spiderman* (2002).

Non-flammable

The house is built of **non-flammable** material so that the fire from the tanks does not spread. A normal house usually burns down in less than an hour, but a scene with a burning house may take days to film. The house needs to remain standing for as long as the film crew needs it.

There's no smoke without fire

This saying is not true for the movies. On-set smoke machines create smoke without fire. Unlike real smoke, the smoke made for movies is safe to breathe in.

Explosions

All kinds of explosions are packed into action movies, such as firing cannons and exploding bombs. Explosives are placed where the explosion is to take place, and then set off from a safe distance.

People must be cleared from a **location** or set before an explosion. A loud alarm gives a warning before explosives are set off.

This snow machine is covering the ground and tombstones in a graveyard, ready for the filming of a winter scene.

Rain

For dry days and indoor filming, rain sometimes has to be made. A pump forces water up a hose and out over the set. Different nozzles are fixed to the hose to create different sizes of raindrops.

Snow

In cold weather, snow is made by spraying water vapour into the air. As the water hits the freezing air, the water freezes into ice crystals, which fall like snow.

Non-melting snow can be made of foam, or a permanent material that is similar to cotton wool.

Wind

To give the effect of either a light sea breeze or a gale, vast amounts of air have to be moved across the set. Depending on the speed of the wind needed, small fans, blowers, or even a jet engine is used.

MUSIC ACTIVITY

Sound effects

Imagine you are a **sound effects** technician and you have to create the sound effects for one of the following digital film sequences.

Steps to follow:

1. Choose from:

a) A horse charging through heavy rain

b) A character drinking a potion and changing into a monster.

2. Think of the sounds you will need to make:

a) rain, and a galloping horse gradually getting louder

b) creepy background noise, rising to a screech, then a growl.

3. Decide how to make the sounds. You could use your voice or instruments.

4. Ask a parent or teacher to help you research sound effects on the Internet.

This boy is using hard plastic cups to make the sound of a horse's hooves. He shakes a paper bag containing rice for rain. For the wind, he simply uses his own mouth to make a blowing noise.

Sets and models

Set-builders and model-makers play a big part in special effects. Weeks of work go into making models for films. The fronts of full-sized buildings are built in studios. Artists build miniatures of spaceships and giant model monsters.

Realism

Sets vary from cityscapes and jungles, to castles and pirate ships. They must be realistic. All the details must be right for **close-up** shots.

The set designer starts by reading the script, then sketching the set for each scene. Costs, possible problems, and materials are discussed. If the movie is set in a specific time in history, the sets need to suit the period. Sometimes a modern-day **location** may have to be adapted. Streets may be made to look Victorian, so they are closed to traffic, and Victorian shop signs are put up.

Real sets combined with **CGI** (see page 24) create this stunning city scene from *The Golden Compass* (2007).

Digital additions

The part of a location that is made into a set is often the place where most of the close-up action takes place. For example, only parts of Skull Island existed in *King Kong* as a set. A whole island – for more distant views – was created digitally.

Scale models

Small-scale models or miniatures of items are filmed so that they appear life-size in the finished movie. A number of model ships were built for use in the movie *Titanic*. One model was 90 per cent of the original ship's size. The models were filmed, and then the people and the smoke from the funnels were added digitally.

This small-scale model was used for filming the distance shots of a sinking cruise ship in the movie, *Titanic* (1997).

The dinosaurs in *Jurassic Park 3* moved along tracks. Machinery opened their sharp-toothed mouths and raised their clawed hands.

Animatronics

Some movie models have to look and move like living beings. Thirty years ago, sophisticated **CGI** technology was not available. So without computer tricks, how could a movie be made starring a dangerous shark?

The answer was to use **animatronics** – robotic puppets operated by remote control. The man-eating animatronic shark in *Jaws* (1975) was rather unrealistic, so it rarely appeared close up in the movie. However, the movie was a box office hit.

Living dinosaurs

Animatronics technology improved – it brought a friendly alien to life in *E.T.* (1982) and deadly dinosaurs appeared in *Jurassic Park* (1993). The full-sized, animatronic dinosaurs were filmed chasing the characters in the movie. The creatures were realistic and frightening. Computer software controlled their moves. Inside a dinosaur, machinery and electronics moved its parts, from its mouth to its eyelids.

3-D animation

3-D animations use 3-D models. Every character is designed and then moulded from a soft material, such as clay and **foam latex** (type of latex used to make masks). For each **frame** (single film shot) of the movie, the artist moves the model slightly. For example, if the character is running, just one step can involve six or seven changes to the limbs of the model.

Painstaking work

Every change of expression in 3-D animations involves detailed work. For example, for a look of surprise, the model's eyebrows are raised, the eyes widened, and the mouth opened. Because the models are small, the filming is close up and every detail must be correct.

In *Wallace and Gromit* movies, tiny changes to the models' mouths and lips are made to match the words they speak.

Sequencing and mixing

Movies are made up of still pictures (stills). When they are put together and shown in the right sequence (order) we see motion. Other, even more interesting effects are achieved by mixing pictures.

Animation

2-D animation films, such as Walt Disney cartoons, are made up of stills. Each still is made by drawing and then colouring an image. Each image is then photographed. When all the photographed images are projected in sequence, a moving story appears. Making a 2-D animated movie takes a lot of work. For just an hour-long film, at least 60,000 images need to be drawn.

Mixing pictures

Showing pictures in the right order is called sequencing. Putting or mixing two or more pictures together is called **compositing**. Compositing is used to put live actors and animated characters together. Also, live actors can be put against a scene they never need to visit.

In the first *King Kong* movie of 1933, actors played in front of a film of a model of the giant ape.

Back projection

An early way of combining films was called back projection. This method was used so that an actor could, for example, appear to be driving a car. While the car seemed to be moving, it was actually static (not moving) in a studio. It was a projected film of a background scene that was actually moving.

In this scene, a separate moving background makes it looks as if Superman is flying.

Behind the actor and car, a big screen was set up and a film of passing countryside, for example, was projected onto the back of the screen. Another camera in front filmed the actor driving the car with the moving scenery behind. The final film combined the two images. Together, they created the effect of the actor driving a car.

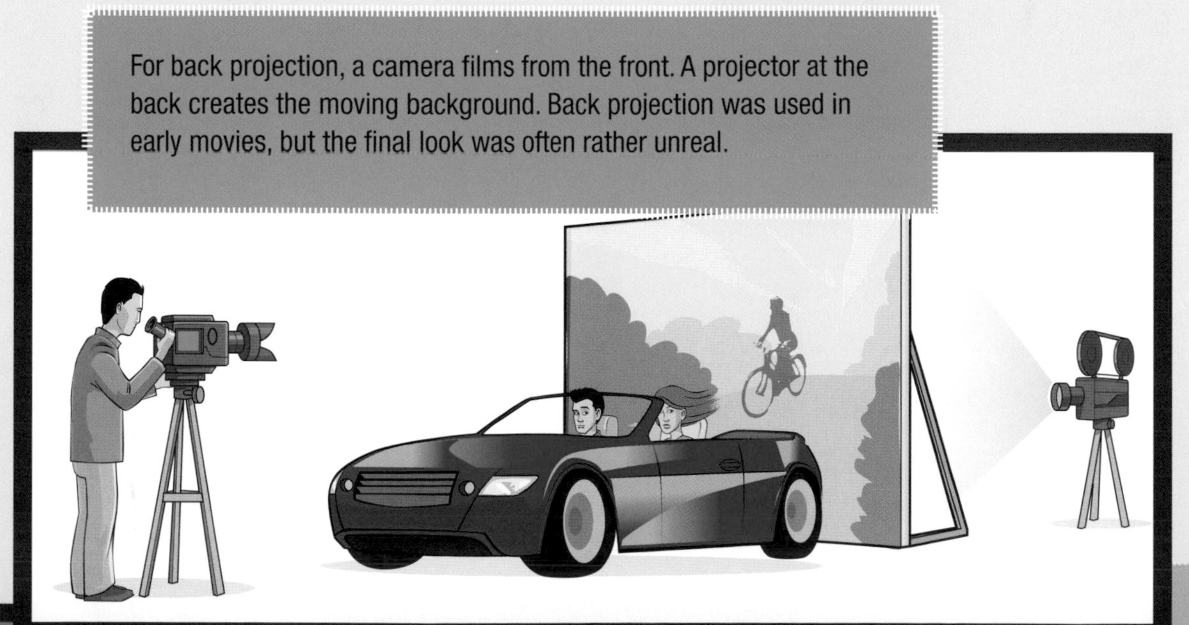

For back projection, a camera films from the front. A projector at the back creates the moving background. Back projection was used in early movies, but the final look was often rather unreal.

This blue screen was replaced with a jungle mountain setting for the movie *King Kong* (2005).

Mattes

Early filmmakers also used a matte ("masking") method in compositing films. Certain parts of what was being filmed first were blocked out with mattes (masks). This was done by putting tape over some of the camera lens or by blocking some of the scene with a blacked out sheet of glass. The masked-out parts did not appear on the film reel and were filled with a second film.

Blue or green screens

Compositing has been much easier with the invention of a special screen, called the blue or green screen. To film a sequence like the giant King Kong grabbing a tiny human heroine, the filmmakers do not need to use tape. Instead, an actress is filmed in front of a green screen. She is suspended in front of the screen and moves as if she is struggling in the hand of the monster. After filming, the blue or green background is removed from the film. Only the actress is left on the film.

A separate digital King Kong is added to the film, so we see his fingers wrapped around the terrified woman.

ART ACTIVITY

Make your own movie

You will need:

- 2 sheets of thin A4 card
- scissors
- pencil and black pen
- stapler

Steps to follow:

1. Place the cards so that the shortest edges are top and bottom. Using a ruler, draw a vertical line down the middle of each card. Draw five horizontal lines to divide each card into ten rectangles, sized 5 cm x 10.5 cm.
2. Cut out the rectangles and write a number on one side of each, 1 to 20.
3. Design a sequence of drawings on a rough sheet of paper. For example, you could draw friends throwing a ball, or a horse jumping over a fence.
4. Put the cards in number order. In pencil, sketch your sequence, with each image progressing further than the last. Draw one picture in the centre of each rectangle.
5. Stack the cards in number order and tightly hold the left-hand edges together. Flick the right-hand edges and check to see if your mini-movie works.
6. Change any pictures you are unhappy with. Next, go over your drawings in a black felt-tipped pen.
7. Staple the left-hand edges together to make a book.

Amazing make-up

Make-up artists and wig makers produce many special effects. They must create fantasy faces and false hair in the form of wigs, beards, and even animal fur! To change the shape of an actor's face or body, **prosthetics** are used. This involves sticking pieces of material on to actors.

Changing faces

Make-up artist Dick Smith was one of the first to get a character to realistically age in a film. In the Western *Little Big Man* (1970) he had to make actor Dustin Hoffman play a character who aged from 17 to 121! It took three hours to apply the make-up to age Hoffman. Smith even made false eyelids from a type of rubber, called **foam latex**, to age the young actor.

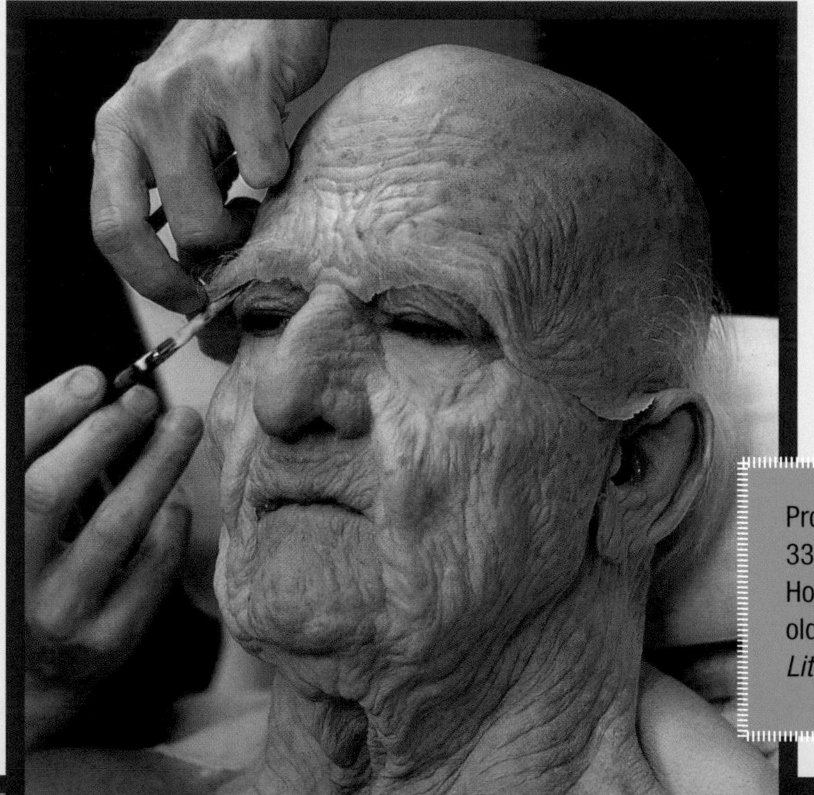

Prosthetics turned 33-year-old Dustin Hoffman into a very old man for his part in *Little Big Man.*

Prosthetics and make-up turned actor Arnold Schwarzenegger into a cyborg (part man and part machine) for the film, *Terminator 2: Judgment Day* (1991).

Prosthetics

To completely change a face or body with prosthetics, first a cast is made of the actor. The cast is used to make a mould. The mould is sculpted into the required shape. The final mould is used to make the paper-thin flexible mask or suit to change the actor's face or body. Sometimes, just small bits of rubber are stuck on an actor, rather than a whole mask or suit.

Creating Voldemort

Actor Ralph Fiennes had to be changed into Voldemort for *Harry Potter and the Order of the Phoenix* (2007). Fiennes' head was reshaped with prosthetic pieces. A temporary tattoo of veins covered his face.

CGI

CGI (computer-generated imagery) is often used for special effects today. It involves creating **3-D** images using computers.

CGI can take the place of dangerous stunts and expensive make-up or **sets**. Large crowd scenes can be computer generated. *The Lord of the Rings* series would have been impossible without CGI. Computers were used to create the 200,000 soldiers in crowd scenes.

CGI animation

CGI can create and bring to life 3-D creatures, such as Aslan in *The Lion, the Witch and the Wardrobe*. To create such a creature, a 3-D model of it is designed on screen first. Points called **controllers** are attached to many different parts of the face and body of the model. Sliders are used to move the points on-screen by hand. For example, sliders move the controllers on Aslan's lips to make him appear to talk. Finally, sequences of the moving creature are combined with the movie film.

It is a time-consuming and painstaking process. For example, Aslan's face alone had 742 controllers.

The Lord of the Rings: The Two Towers (2002) won awards for its CGI effects, including for this battle scene.

An actor moves around like the character of Gollum. His movements are "captured" and used to bring the CGI character of Gollum to life.

Gollum, from *The Lord of the Rings* films, was created using a puppet, CGI, and motion capture.

Motion capture

Motion capture makes computer-generated people or creatures appear to move realistically. First, a model is created as above. An actor then acts out whatever movements are required, such as the strange movements of a character like Gollum in *The Lord of the Rings*. The actor wears a suit with reflective dots all over it. Cameras and computers record the movement of the dots as the actor moves around. The recordings are used to program the movement of the sliders on the 3-D computer-generated model.

Morphing

Sometimes in movies, we see people and creatures change shape or turn to dust. For example, a character in *Indiana Jones and the Last Crusade* (1989) ages and turns to dust in seconds.

Originally, such a change (called a morph) was created by filming a sequence of different images of the actor. The images were taken at different stages as make-up was applied. The before, in-between, and final images of the morph were then dissolved together to create a smooth sequence.

Computer blends

The more realistic transformations in movies today are the work of computers and CGI. Computer programs can blend images that are completely different. For example, separate images of a man and a robot can be morphed into one blended image. The software also produces morphing sequences that look realistic, even when viewed in slow motion. In *The Incredible Hulk* (2008), the hero morphs into a muscular giant. New computer programs made the growth of his muscles look realistic.

This picture shows the final stage in the morph from man to monster-like giant in *The Incredible Hulk*.

PERFORMANCE ACTIVITY

Who are you talking to?

CGI characters often have to be added after the film has been shot. This means that actors have to perform while pretending a character is standing in front of them.

Imagine you are starring in a movie about aliens. You are rehearsing a scene in which an alien has just appeared! It is talking to you and walking around you.

Steps to follow:

1. Get a fixed image of the alien in your mind. Decide how tall it is, whether it is friendly or scary, and how it moves.
2. Now imagine how you would feel (shaky legs, clammy hands, fast-beating heart, dry mouth).
3. Think about what you would say and your tone of voice.
4. Now rehearse the scene. Remember to direct your gaze at where the alien's face might be.
5. Ask a friend to watch. Can you convince your friend that there is another "presence" in the room?

This boy sees a green, long fingered invader and screams out! What does your alien look like? What will you say?

Award winners

The Academy Awards, also known as the Oscars, include an Oscar for visual effects. Here are the winners for the visual effects awards, 2001–09.

As well as real and virtual actors, 400 cardboard cut-outs of people were used in crowd scenes for the film *Gladiator*.

2001 *Gladiator* – 2,000 live actors were used to create a **CGI** crowd of 35,000 virtual actors. Film released in 2000.

2002 *The Lord of the Rings: The Fellowship of the Ring* – An effect called forced perspective was used to make the little hobbits look smaller than the giant Gandalf. Gandalf stayed closer to the camera so that he appeared to be much taller. Film released in 2001.

2003/4 *The Lord of the Rings: The Two Towers* and *The Return of the King* – It took more than 1,000 drawings and 100 sculptures to design the character of Gollum. Films released in 2002 and 2003.

2005	*Spider-Man 2* – Effects included an amazing puppet-controlled set of tentacles, attached to the character Doctor Octopus. Four people operated each long tentacle. Film released in 2004.
2006	*King Kong* – The digitally created 1930s New York **set** included 90,000 separate buildings. Film released in 2005.
2007	*Pirates of the Caribbean: Dead Man's Chest* – This movie had 1,100 special visual effects shots (the average for films is 200). Film released in 2006.
2008	*The Golden Compass* – CGI animals appeared in nearly every scene, including a fight between two bears with 100 other bears watching. Film released in 2007.
2009	*The Curious Case of Benjamin Button* – CGI was used to make Brad Pitt's character gradually age backwards. Film released in 2008.

CGI polar bears battle it out in *The Golden Compass.*

Glossary

2-D two dimensional. A 2-D shape has just two dimensions (length and width).

3-D three dimensional. A 3-D shape has three dimensions (length, width, and depth).

animation moving images made up of frames. Animations vary from simply drawn cartoons, to complex feature films using life-like models.

animatronics using robots and electronics to make realistic, moving animals. Life-like dinosaurs can be made with animatronics.

atmosphere feel of a place. A misty dark forest has a creepier atmosphere than a sunlit beach.

CGI computer generated imagery is the use of computers to create images

close-up camera shot taken close to the person or object being filmed

compositing putting several images together. Compositing a background and a foreground gives a complete picture.

controllers points on a computer model of a character that can be moved

digital effects effects made on computers after a film has been shot, or the effects found throughout a CGI film

foam latex flexible, rubbery material. Model creatures in animations often have flexible foam latex joints.

frame single film shot, like a photograph. Movies are made of lots of frames, shown one after the other.

location where action in a film occurs

mechanical effects effects filmed on set that use real objects, people, and machinery

non-flammable cannot be burned easily

prosthetics make-up process that involves gluing material to an actor. A mask is made by a prosthetics artist.

pyrotechnician expert on fires and explosions. They can safely create a house fire that does not burn the house down or put the actors in danger.

set scenery built in a studio or on location for filming

sound effect sound used in a movie. Orcs screeching in *The Lord of the Rings* was made using opossum noises.

stunt co-ordinator technician who ensures stunts are realistic and safe

stunt performer person who does the dangerous bits in a movie. They are trained not to hurt themselves or others.

Find out more

Books

The Secret Science Behind Movie Stunts and Special Effects, Steve Wolf (Skyhorse Publishing, 2007)

Websites

www.rhythm.com
Click on "Design" to see examples of works such as mattes by a special effects team.

http://entertainment.howstuffworks.com/question295
This site explains how special effects are created.

Places to visit

BFI IMAX cinema
1 Charlie Chaplin Walk
South Bank
Waterloo
London
SE1 8XR
Tel: +44 (0)20 7928 3232
www.bfi.org.uk

See 2D movies, 3D movies, and special effects at their best on the biggest screen in the UK.

Index

2-D animations 18
3-D animations 17
3-D images 24
3-D models 17, 24

animals, talking 5, 24
animatronics 16

back projection 19
best-effects awards 28–29
blue or green screen 20
brain 4

car chases 8
car rolls 8
Casino Royale 8
CGI 5, 14, 16, 24–25, 26–29
  computer blends 26
  computer software 16, 26
  controllers 24
  motion capture 25, 29
close-up shots 6, 14, 15
compositing 18, 20
crowd scenes 24, 28

Die Another Day 8
digital effects 5, 15

ejection 7
E.T. 16
Execution of Mary, Queen of Scots, The 5
explosions 11

falls 7
fires 10–11
first ever special effects 5
flight 7
foam latex 17, 22
forced perspective 28
frames 17

Gladiator 28
Golden Compass, The 14, 29

Harry Potter and the Order of the Phoenix 23
horse's hooves 13

Incredible Hulk, The 26
Indiana Jones and the Last Crusade 26

Jaws 16
Jurassic Park 3, 16

King Kong 15, 18, 20, 29

Lion, The Witch, and The Wardrobe, The 5, 24
Little Big Man 22
locations 14, 15
Lord of the Rings, The 24–25, 28–29

make-up 22, 23
make your own movie 21
mattes 20
mechanical effects 5
mixing pictures 18–20
model-makers 14
models
  3-D models 17, 24
  scale models 15
morphing 26
motion capture 25, 29

non-flammable materials 10

Oscars (Academy Awards) 28–29

Pirates of the Caribbean: Dead Man's Chest 29
props 9
prosthetics 22, 23, 29
pyrotechnicians 10

rain 12, 13
ramps 7, 8
realism 14

safety 8, 9
safety glass 9
sequencing 18
sets 5, 10, 15
  designers 14
  set-builders 14
smoke machines 11
snow 12
snow machines 12
sound effects 13
Spiderman movies 7, 10, 29
stills 18
storms 10
stunt co-ordinators 6
stunt performers 5, 6, 7, 9
  skills 9
  training courses 9
stunts 6–9
Superman 19

Terminator 2: Judgment Day 23
Titanic 15

Wallace and Grommit 17
Walt Disney cartoons 18
wig-makers 22
wind 12, 13
Wizard of Oz, The 4